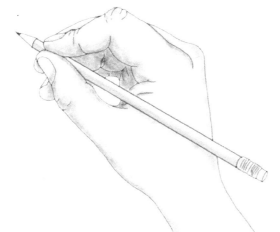

How to
Draw Animals

40 Step-by-Step Drawing Projects

Alisa Calder

Drawing 101

Have you always wanted to learn to draw but didn't know where to start? Learning to draw can seem overwhelming, but by using the step-by-step method you will soon be drawing better than you thought possible.

This book contains tutorials that will teach you how to draw all types of animals including birds, cats, ducks, pigs, elephants, butterflies, and many more. Each step-by-step tutorial will guide you from the first step to the finished drawing.

Each diagram on the left shows you how to draw the object one step at a time. Simply follow along drawing in the space provided on the right-hand side. Add each detail as shown until the picture is finished.

Start off drawing lightly and don't worry about making mistakes. You can always erase and start over.

When you're finished, you can add your own details and color it if you wish.

How to Draw Animals: 40 Step-by-Step Drawing Projects is perfect for beginners who want to quickly gain a sense of mastery in their drawing. Suitable for children, teens, and adults who want to practice and improve their drawing skills.

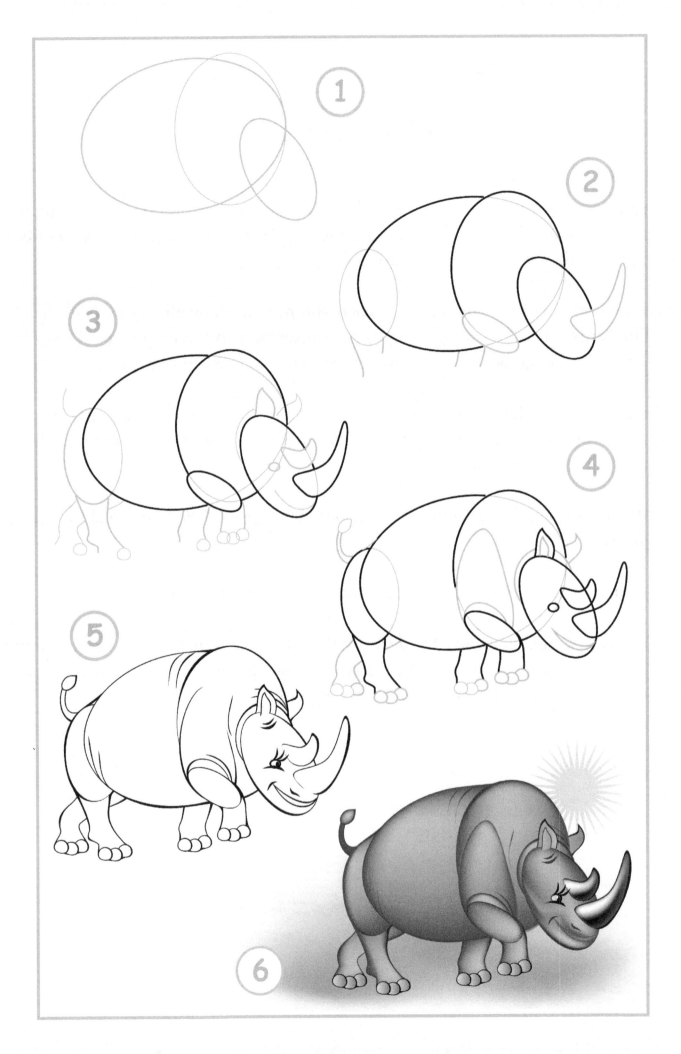

Practice Drawing Space

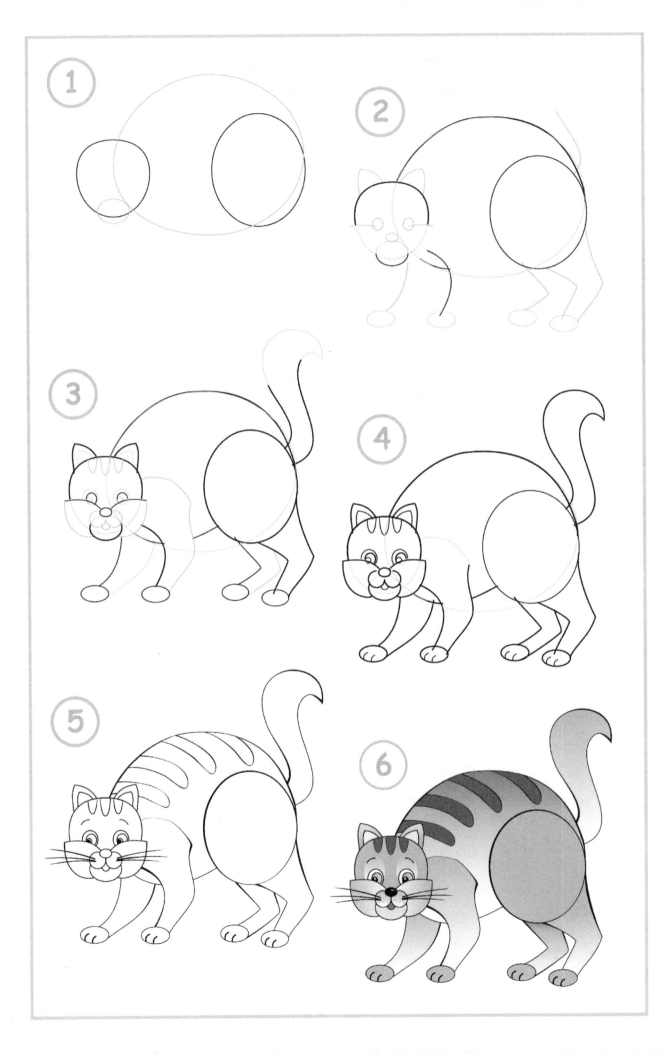

Practice Drawing Space

Practice Drawing Space

Practice Drawing Space

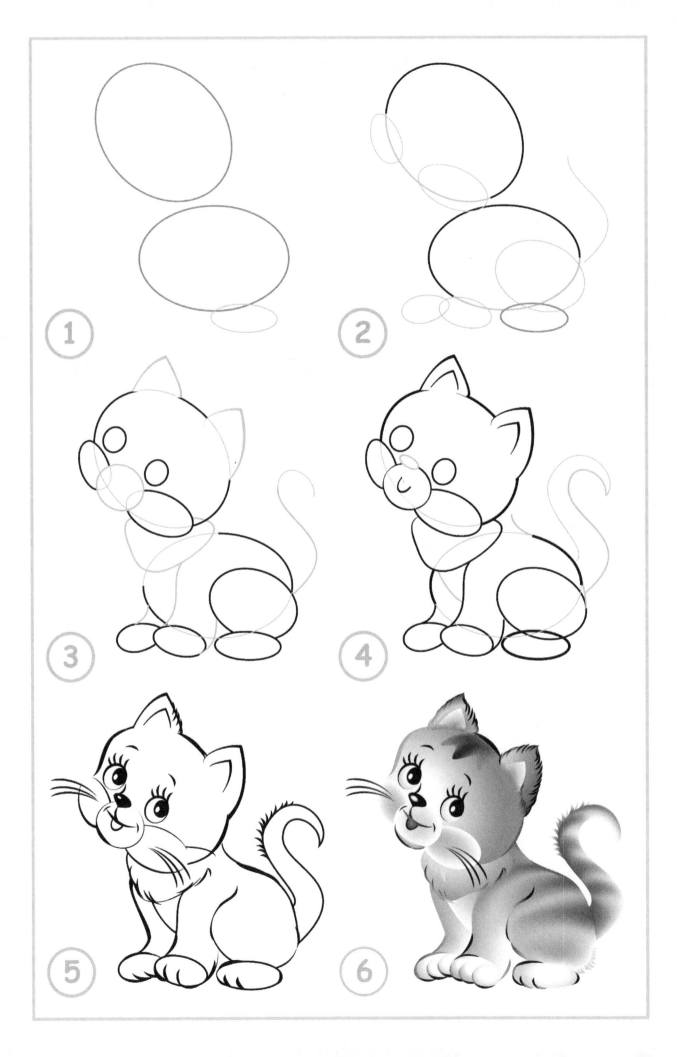

Practice Drawing Space

Practice Drawing Space

Practice Drawing Space

Practice Drawing Space

Practice Drawing Space

Practice Drawing Space

Practice Drawing Space

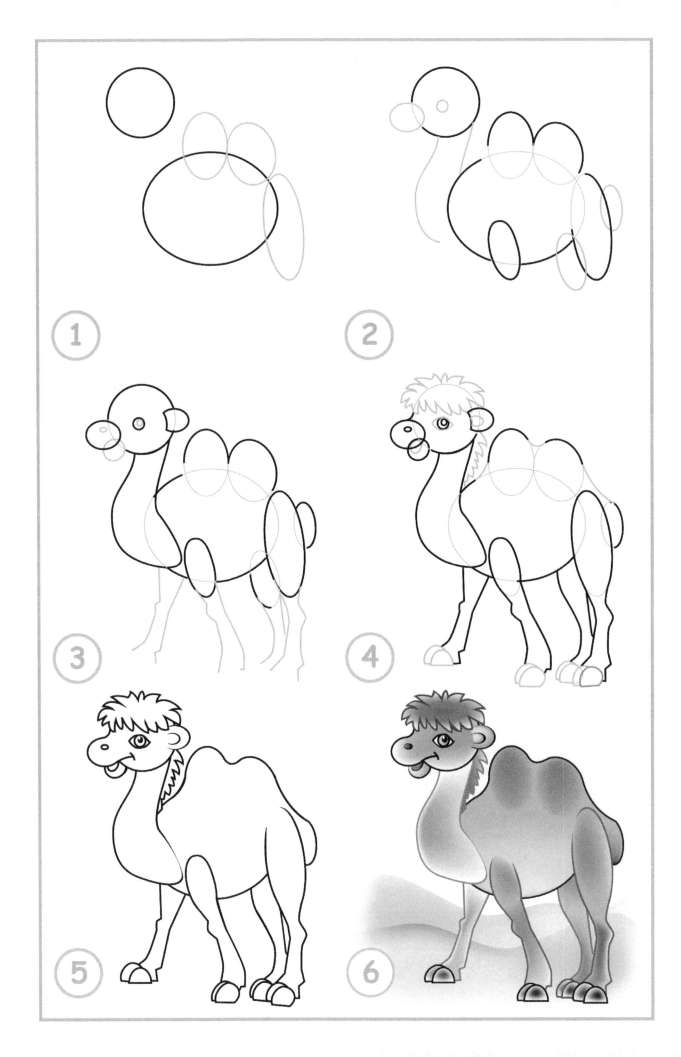

Practice Drawing Space

Practice Drawing Space

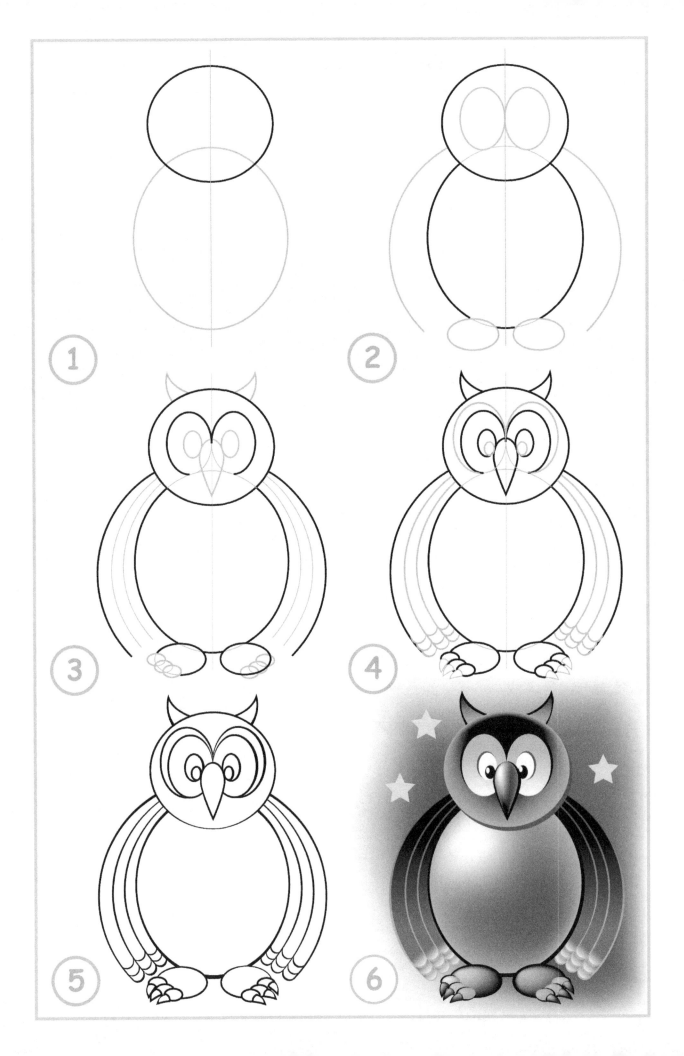

Practice Drawing Space

Practice Drawing Space

Practice Drawing Space

Practice Drawing Space

Practice Drawing Space

Practice Drawing Space

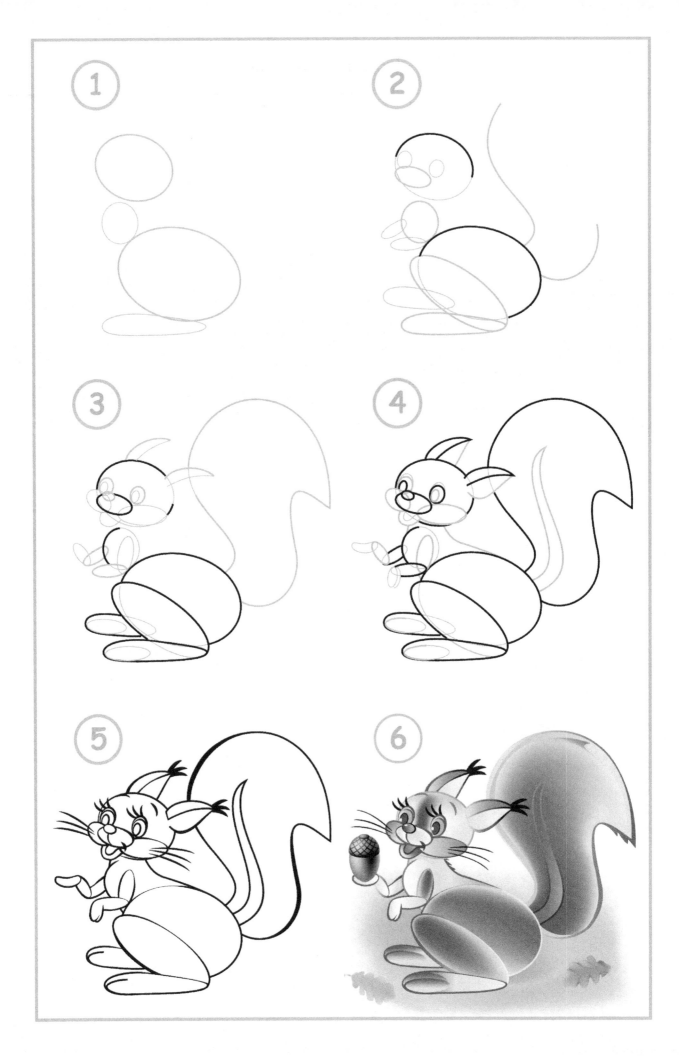

Practice Drawing Space

Practice Drawing Space

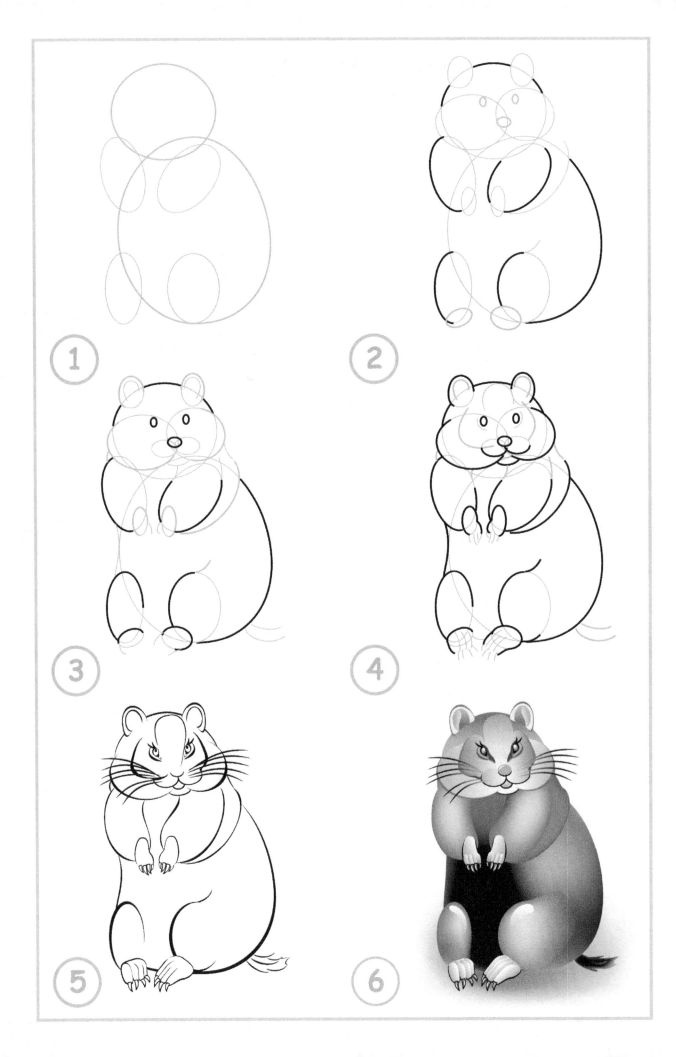

Practice Drawing Space

1

2

3

4

5

6

Practice Drawing Space

Practice Drawing Space

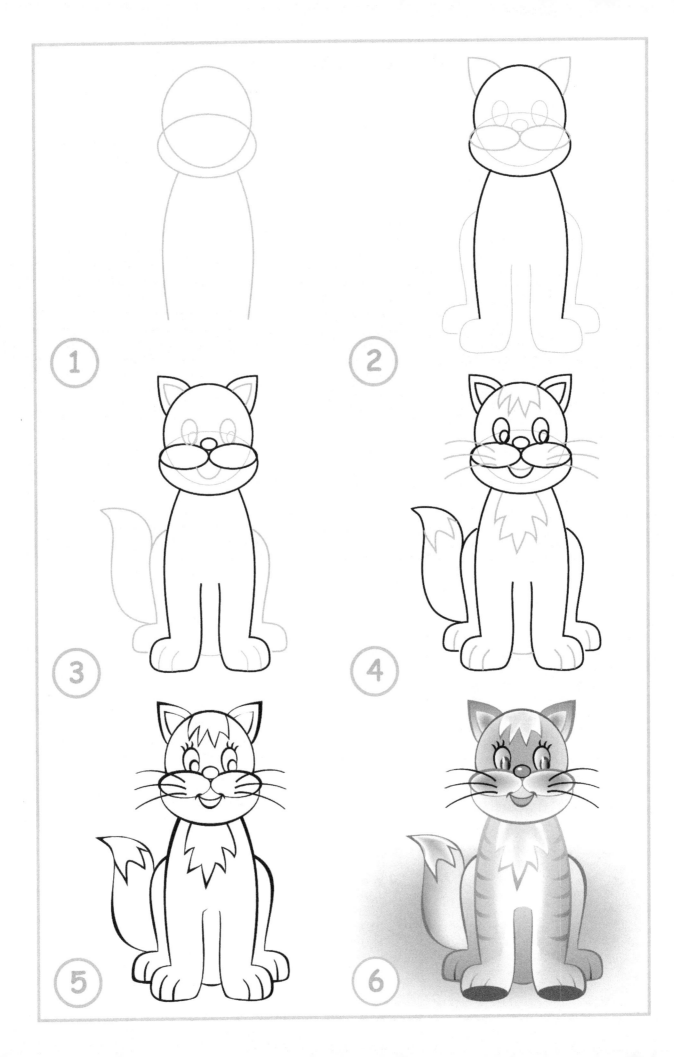

1

2

3

4

5

6

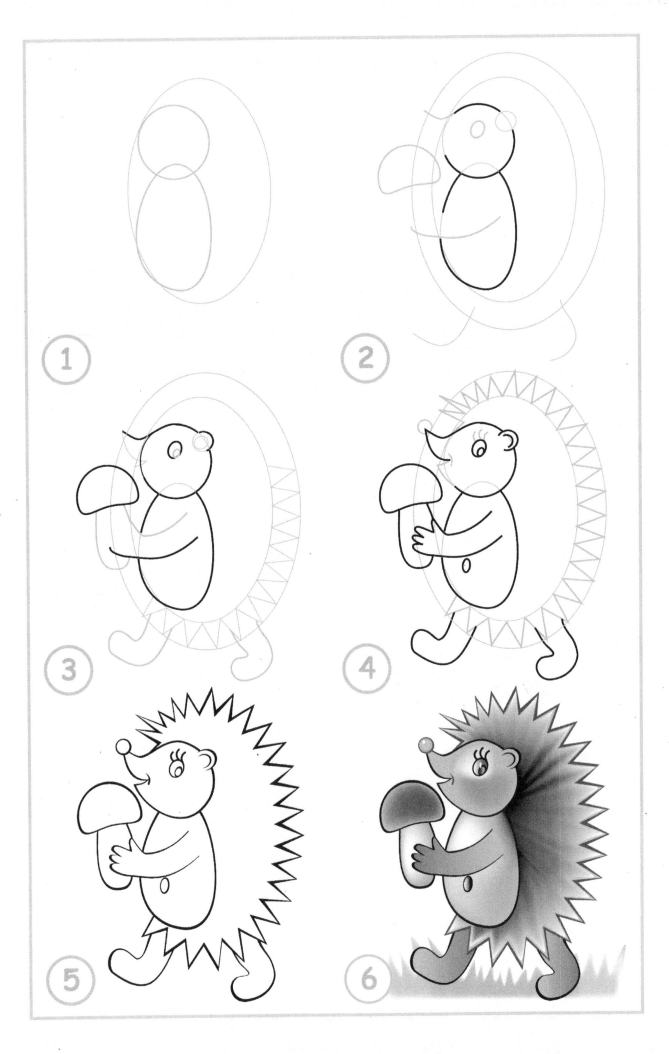

①　②　③　④　⑤　⑥

Practice Drawing Space

Practice Drawing Space

Practice Drawing Space

Practice Drawing Space

Practice Drawing Space

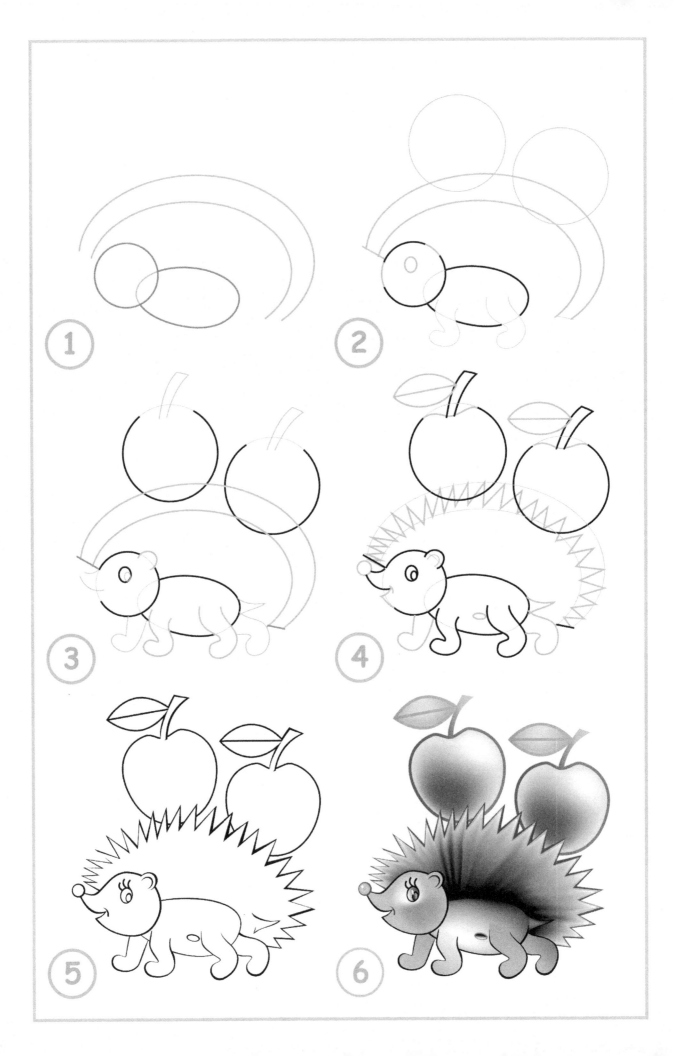

Practice Drawing Space

Practice Drawing Space

Practice Drawing Space

Practice Drawing Space

Practice Drawing Space

Practice Drawing Space

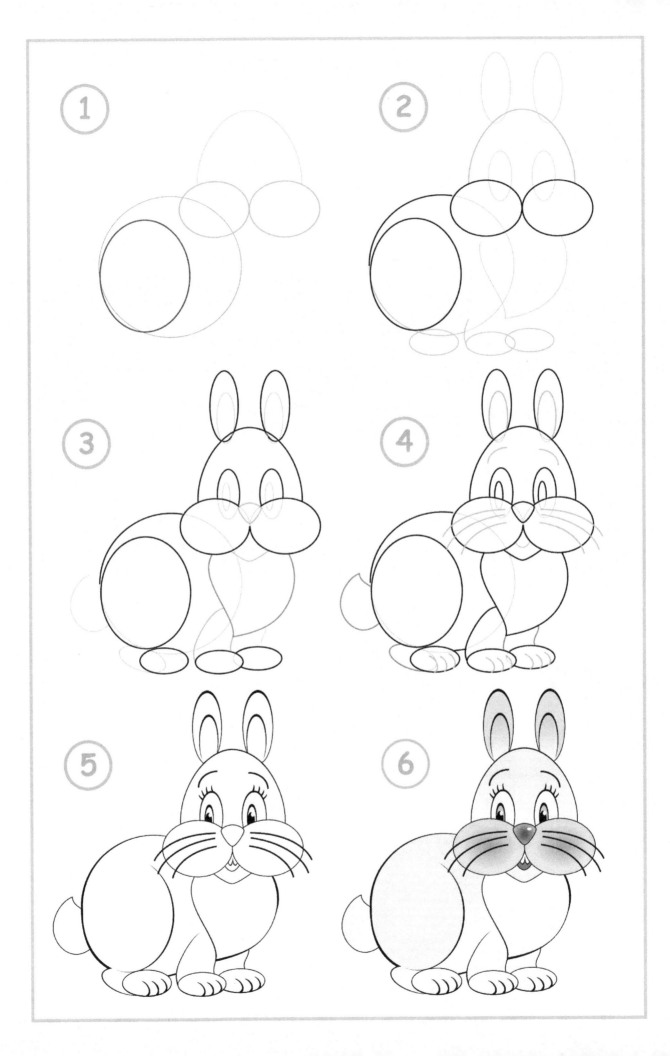

Practice Drawing Space

Made in the USA
Monee, IL
05 December 2023

48217696R00046